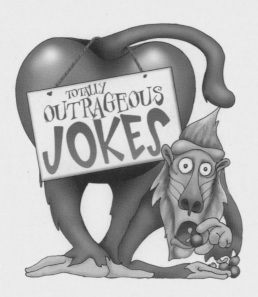

Compiled by Karen King
Design layout by Chalk & Cheese

TOP THAT!™

Published by Top That! Publishing
Tide Mill Way, Woodbridge, Suffolk, IP12 1AP
www.topthatpublishing.com
Copyright © 2002 Top That! Publishing plc
Top That! is a Registered Trade Mark of Top That! Publishing

Why did the chicken
cross the road?
To get to the other side.

What do baby apes
sleep in?
Apricots.

Why couldn't the
orange get up
the hill?
It ran out of juice.

What is black and
white and read
all over?
A newspaper.

How do frogs cross
the road?
They follow the Green
Cross Toad.

Why do bees hum?
They can't remember
the words.

Where do you find
giant snails?
At the end of giant fingers.

What happened to the cat that swallowed a ball of wool?
She had mittens.

Where do sheep get their hair cut?
At the baa-baa shop.

Why is the sky so high?
So the birds don't bump their heads.

Who was the first underwater spy?
James Pond.

Why do hens watch TV?
To be hentertained.

What do you say if you meet a toad?
Wart's new?

Which animal didn't go in the ark in pairs?
Maggots – they went in apples.

What's green, prickly and goes up and down?
A gooseberry in a lift.

What goes woof woof tick?
A watch dog.

How do chickens dance?
Chick to chick.

What do jelly babies wear when it's raining?
Gumboots.

What do you call a sleeping bull?
A bulldozer.

How do you keep an elephant from smelling?
Tie a knot in it's trunk.

What do you call a high rise home for pigs?
A styscraper.

Where do pigs sleep?
In hammocks.

What do birds
watch on TV?
The feather
forecast.

What's the most
famous fish?
The starfish.

What do you give
a pig with a
sore throat?
Oinkment.

Knock! Knock!
Who's there?
Lettuce.
Lettuce who?
Lettuce in and you'll
find out.

What can you serve but not eat?
A tennis ball.

Where do you
pick up bees?
At a buzz stop.

How does Jack
Frost get to work?
By icicle.

What do you call a spider with no legs?
A currant.

5

What is the same size
as an elephant but
weighs nothing?
An elephant's shadow.

What do you get if
you cross a clock with
a joker?
A laugh a minute.

Why do cows
have bells?
Because their horns
don't work.

What is the best advice to
give a worm?
Sleep late.

What do you get if you cross a mouse with
a bar of soap?
Bubble and squeak.

What did the traffic light
say to the car?
Don't look now, I'm
changing.

Why don't
cats shave?
Because eight out
of ten prefer
whiskers.

Why aren't barbers ever late for work?
Because they know all the short cuts.

What do you get if you
sit under a cow?
A pat on the head.

What's the laziest
mountain in
the world?
Mount Ever-rest.

What nuts can you
hang pictures on?
Walnuts.

What has an eye
but can't see?
A needle.

How do you join the police force?
Handcuff them together.

What sort of bow is
impossible to tie?
A rainbow.

What did the lollipop
say to the boy?
"Hello, sucker".

What did the envelope say to the stamp?
Stick with me and we'll go places.

Did you hear the joke
about the dustbin?
It's a load of rubbish.

Did you hear the joke
about the lump
of coal?
Better not tell you -
it's too dirty.

Did you hear about the woman who washed
her front doorstep?
She broke her washing machine.

What has four legs and a trunk?
A mouse on holiday.

When is an English
teacher like a judge?
When she hands out
long sentences.

What's the best
thing to put in
a pizza?
Your teeth.

What's a
hedgehog's
favourite food?
Prickled onions.

How do you get
a ghost to lie
perfectly flat?
You use a spirit level.

"Knock! Knock!"
"Who's there?"
"Eskimo."
"Eskimo who?"
"Eskimo questions, I'll tell
you no lies."

Why did the pilot
land the aeroplane
on the house roof?
Because the man had
left the landing
light on.

What did the mother ghost say to the naughty
baby ghosts.
Speak when you're spooken to.

Did you hear about the
cross-eyed teacher?
She had no control over
her pupils.

Why wouldn't the
skeleton go to school?
Because his heart wasn't
in it.

Did you hear about the brilliant geography teacher? He had abroad knowledge of his subject.

What do you get if you cross a helicopter with a shark? A helichopper.

What kind of ghosts haunt hospitals? Surgical spirits.

What does a cow with hiccups give you? A milk shake.

Why did the maths teacher marry the school cleaner? Because she swept him right off his feet.

What did the big telephone say to the little telephone? You're too young to be engaged.

Did you hear about the two peanuts walking down Piccadilly? One was a-salted.

What do you get
if you cross a
mouse with
an orange?
A pip squeak.

Why did the teacher
have her hair in
a bun?
Because she had her
nose in a hamburger.

What position do ghosts
play in football?
Ghoulie.

Why did the robot
act stupid?
Because he had a
screw loose.

What goes red, green, red,
green, red, green?
A frog in a liquidiser.

What goes 99 bonk,
99 bonk?
A centipede with a
wooden leg.

What's small,
green and does
good deeds?
A cub sprout.

11

How does a monster count to 13?
By using its fingers.

What's worse than finding a maggot in an apple?
Finding half a maggot.

What time is it when an elephant sits on your fence?
Time to get a new one.

Why do stupid people eat biscuits?
Because they're crackers.

Who delivers presents to baby sharks at Christmas?
Santa Jaws.

What did the sea say to the sand?
Nothing, it just waved.

Why can't a car play football?
Because it only has one boot.

Where do fish keep their money?
In the river bank.

What is the definition
of a doughnut?
A crazy millionaire.

Why did the tortoise
cross the road?
To go to the shell shop.

What did the man say
when he walked into
the bar?
Ouch!

What do vampires
like for lunch?
Fangfurters.

Where do ghosts go on holiday?
The Isle of Fright.

What's the heaviest
part of a fish?
Its scales.

Jane: "Knock, knock".
Sue: Who's there?
Jane: "See, you've
forgotten me already."

What's the best place
to find diamonds?
In a pack of cards.

Which side of a cup
is the handle on?
The outside.

Why was the little bird
expelled from school?
She kept playing
practical yolks.

What do you do with
a blue banana?
Try and cheer it up.

Why did the bus stop?
Because it saw a
zebra crossing.

My sister is so dim
she thinks that a
cartoon is a song
you sing in a car.

What is white, furry
and has a hole in the
middle of it?
A polo bear.

Why did the
tomato blush?
Because it saw the
salad dressing.

Tom: "It's raining cats
and dogs."
Jim: "Well, make sure you
don't step in a poodle."

What do you get if you cross
a kangaroo with a sheep?
14   A woolly jumper.

Why do vampires never get fat?
They eat necks to nothing.

Why were the two flies playing football in the saucer?
They were practising for the cup.

Did you hear the joke about the butter?
I better not tell you, you might spread it.

Did you hear about the hyena who swallowed an ice cube?
He made a laughing stock of himself.

Why did the teacher put on her sunglasses?
Because her pupils were too bright.

What's big, grey and fast?
An elephant on roller skates.

What house weighs the least?
A lighthouse.

What does a headless horse ride?
A nightmare.

What does a penguin
pay for its dinner?
Six squid.

What do you feed
a dinosaur?
Whatever it wants.

Did you hear the joke
about the high wall?
I'd better not tell you
– you might not get
over it.

What happens when
a band plays in a
thunderstorm?
The conductor gets
hit by lightning.

Did you hear about
the wooden car?
It had wooden wheels,
wooden windows and
wooden go.

Why are penguins such
good racing drivers?
Because they are in a
pole position.

Why does a stork stand on one leg?
Because it would fall over if it lifted the other one.

What is a tornado?
Mother nature doing
the twist.

What do you do with a
sick wasp?
Take it to the waspital.

What sort of ship does
Count Dracula sail on?
A blood vessel.

Doctor, doctor, I
think I'm a fly.
Well, buzz off then.

How did the baker get an electric shock?
He stood on a bun and a currant ran up his leg.

Are vampires mad?
Well, they're often bats.

What do cats read
every morning?
Mewspapers.

How do you
get freckles?
Sunbathe under
a sieve.

What fish tastes best
with ice cream?
A jellyfish.

My dog saw a sign
that said:
'Wet Paint' - so he did.

Where do cows go
for an evening out?
To the moo-vies.

What do cats like
for breakfast?
Mice Krispies.

What do you call a
woodpecker with no beak?
A head banger.

What's thick, black, floats on water and
shouts "Knickers!"?
Crude oil.

On which side
has a chicken got
more feathers?
On the outside.

What runs but has no legs?
A tap.

What's black and white
and makes a lot of noise?
A zebra with a set
of drums.

What is the dead
centre of a town?
A cemetery.

18

What's red and goes beep, beep?
A strawberry in a traffic jam.

What is a snail?
A slug with a crash helmet.

What goes through the water at a 100 miles per hour?
A motor pike.

What wears a coat all winter and pants all summer?
A dog.

Why do we plant bulbs in the garden?
So the worms can see where they're going.

What happened when the cows escaped from their field?
There was udder chaos.

What lives in apples and is an avid reader?
A bookworm.

What's big, grey and wobbles at the knees?
A jellyphant.

What do you get if you cross an elephant with a skunk?
A big stinker.

What do you call a skeleton that's always sleeping?
Lazy bones.

What's round, white and laughs a lot?
A tickled onion.

Why did the hedgehog cross the road?
To see his flatmate.

Why did the monster eat a lightbulb?
Because he needed some light refreshment.

What do you get if you cross an elephant with a mouse?
Big holes in your skirting board.

What did the stupid monster call his pet tiger?
Spot.

What time did the Chinaman go to the dentist?
Tooth-hurtie.

"Doctor, doctor, I think I'm invisible."
"Who said that?"

How does Dracula keep fit?
He plays batminton.

Why did the monster take his nose apart?
To see what made it run.

What do cows have for breakfast?
Moos-li.

What bird is always out of breath?
A puffin.

How do you start a pudding race?
Sago.

How do farmers count their cows?
They use cowculators.

What do you get if you cross a cat with a lemon?
A sourpuss.

What's the best thing to give a seasick elephant?
Plenty of room.

What do you get if you
cross a galaxy with
a toad?
Star Warts.

What's the
strongest creature in
the ocean?
A mussel.

What did the big
chimney say to
the little chimney?
You're too young
to smoke.

Why was the mother
kangaroo cross with
her children?
Because they ate
crisps in bed.

What do you call a
man with a seagull on
his head?
Cliff.

"Doctor, doctor,
everyone keeps
ignoring me."
"Next!"

What's a cannibal's
favourite game?
Swallow my leader.

What do you call a man
with a spade on his head?
Doug.

Why are false teeth
like stars?
They come out
at night.

Why couldn't the two
elephants go swimming?
Because they only had one
pair of trunks.

What is a dimple?
A pimple going the
wrong way.

What's a skeleton's
favourite instrument?
A trombone.

How do you get milk from a cat?
Take away its saucer.

How many skunks does it
take to make a big stink?
A phew!

What's worse than a
bull in a china shop?
A hedgehog in a
balloon factory.

Why did the fly dance on the jam jar lid?
Because it said 'Twist to open'.

Why are sheep
like pubs?
They're full of baas.

Where do spiders
play football?
Webley.

What kind of
jokes does a
chiropodist like?
Corny jokes.

Did you hear about
the stupid tap dancer?
He fell in the sink.

What's the best way of stopping a monster
from sliding through the eye of a needle?
Tie a knot in its neck.

What is hairy and coughs?
A coconut with a cold.

What do you call a
thin mouse?
A narrow squeak.

What dance do two
tins do?
The can-can.

What's the best thing
to take into the desert?
A thirst-aid kit.

24

Which town in Britain makes terrible sandwiches?
Oldham.

What do you call a crazy kangaroo?
Hopping mad.

What's big, hairy and can fly very fast?
King Kongcorde.

How do you stop a werewolf howling in the back of your car?
Put him in the front.

What's an insect's favourite game?
Cricket.

Why don't elephants eat penguins?
Because they can't get the wrappers off.

Where do witches' frogs sit?
On toadstools.

When is it bad luck to be followed by a black cat?
When you're a mouse.

What can you make that can't be seen?
A noise.

What is the
loudest game?
Tennis, because you
need a racket to play.

"Have you any
invisible ink?"
"Certainly, Sir.
What colour?"

What fish can sing?
The tuna fish.

If two shirt colours
had a race, which
one would win?
Neither. It would end
in a tie.

What did the biscuit
say as it rolled down
the hill?
"Oh, crumbs!"

What can you keep and give
away at the same time?
A cold.

Which vegetable
goes best with
jacket potatoes?
Button mushrooms.

Why didn't the dinosaur
cross the road?
Because roads hadn't
been invented.

What is big, grey
and mutters?
A mumbo jumbo.

What happened when
the idiot had a
brain transplant?
The brain rejected him.

What do you get if you
cross a centipede and
a parrot?
A walkie-talkie.

What do you call a
donkey with only
three legs?
A wonky.

What happened to the man who put his
false teeth in backwards?
He ate himself.

What game do little
ghosts play at parties?
Haunt the thimble.

Who makes suits and
eats spinach?
Popeye the Tailorman.

A bird in the hand can
make a terrible mess.

What's a giant's
favourite tale?
A tall story.

What did the shy pebble say? "I wish I was a little boulder."

Why didn't the skeleton jump off the cliff? Because he had no guts.

What do you do if your nose goes on strike? Picket.

What do you call a road with diamonds down the middle? A jewel carriageway.

How many balls of string does it take to reach the Moon? One if it's long enough.

Where do ghouls go to study? Ghoullege.

What do you call a Teletubby that's been burgled? A Tubby.

Why did the child take a sledgehammer to school? It was the day they broke up.

How do you make a
band stand?
Take away their chairs.

What do you call a
gorilla that swings
from shop to shop?
A meringue-utang.

Why does a golfer
need a spare pair
of shoes?
In case he gets a
hole in one.

"Knock! Knock!"
"Who's there?"
"Alec."
"Alec who?"
"Alec a nice cup of
tea, please."

What do you call a man
who's already around
when you want him?
Andy.

What do you call a
zebra with no stripes?
A horse.

What's an Ig?
An Eskimo's house
without a toilet.

What did the puddle say
to the rain?
Why don't you drop
in sometime.

What happens when you throw a green stone in the Red Sea?
It gets wet.

"Knock! Knock!"
"Who's there?"
"Little boy who can't reach the doorbell!"

Why did the plumber go into the garden?
To mend the leeks.

Why are ghosts so bad at lying?
You can see straight through them.

Why is a baby like an old car?
They both have a rattle.

What is a net?
Holes tied together with string.

Why are rivers rich?
Because they have two banks.

What do monkeys sing at Christmas?
"Jungle bells, jungle bells ..."

What's small, furry and cuts corn?
A combine hamster.

What's red and
stupid?
A blood clot.

What smells, has four
wheels and flies?
A dustcart.

What's a horse's
favourite sport?
Stable tennis.

What is parrot
food called?
Pollyfilla.

What sort of fish can't swim?
A dead one.

Why was the sand wet?
Because the seaweed.

How do fish travel
from one place
to another?
On the whale way.

How long should a
horse's legs be?
Long enough to reach
the ground.

Why are brides
unlucky?
They never marry the
best man.

31

What do you call a
disastrous cat?
A catastrophe.

Why was the
insect kicked out
of the park?
Because it was a
litterbug.

What do you do if
you split your sides
laughing?
Run until you get a
stitch.

"Doctor, doctor, I've
got a little stye."
"Well you'd better
buy a little pig."

What do you call five
bottles of lemonade?
A pop group.

Why did the
elephant leave the
circus?
He was tired of
working for peanuts.

How do fleas travel
from one place to
another?
By itch hiking.

What kind of ghosts
haunt hospitals?
Surgical spirits.

What do you get if you cross a sheep dog and a bunch of daisies?
Collie-flowers.

Which day of the week do ghosts like best?
Moandays.

What's the difference between a vampire and a biscuit?
You can't dip a vampire in your tea.

What are horse's favourite exams?
Haylevels.

Why did the composer spend all his time in bed?
He wrote sheet music.

What do you call a deer with no eyes?
No idea.

What do you call a deer with no eyes and no legs?
Still no idea.

Did you hear the one
about the cornflakes?
I'll tell you next week,
it's a cereal.

What would happen
if pigs could fly?
Bacon would go up.

What goes up and
doesn't come down?
Your age.

Which famous artist
used to sit on ice cubes?
Bottichilli.

What's the best way
to cover a cushion?
Sit on it.

What starts with a T,
ends with a T and is
full of T?
A teapot.

Who invented fire?
A bright spark.

What did Noah use to
light his Ark?
Floodlights.

When does Friday come
before Thursday?
In the dictionary.

34

What's green and
bounces around
the garden?
A spring onion.

"Knock, Knock!"
"Who's there?"
"Boo."
"Boo who?"
"There's no need to cry,
it's only a joke."

How did they know that the Jaws
victim had dandruff?
He left his head and shoulders on the beach.

Why is gossip like a kiss?
It passes from mouth
to mouth.

What swings from
cake to cake?
Tarzipan.

What's the difference between stork and butter?
Butter can't stand on one leg.

What's big and grey and has
sixteen wheels?
An elephant on roller skates.

What's black and
white and red all over?
A zebra on a sunbed.

35

Why did Robin Hood
only steal from the rich?
Because the poor had
nothing worth stealing.

Why do birds fly
south in winter?
Because it's too far
to walk.

What fruit is
found in a stable?
A strawberry.

What animal do you
look like when you
have a bath?
A little bear.

Why do French
people eat snails?
Because they don't
like fast food.

What do you find in
a gum tree?
A stick insect.

Why do bees have
sticky hair?
They use
honeycombs.

How does a witch tell
the time?
She uses a witchwatch.

If two's company and three's a crowd, what are four and five?
Nine.

Who was the fastest runner in the world?
Adam, He was the first in the human race.

What do you get if you cross an egg white with gunpowder?
Boom-meringue.

What makes a glow-worm glow?
A light meal.

Thieves have stolen a van full of wigs. Police are combing the area.

When did only three vowels exist?
Before you and I were born.

Why did the robber take a bath?
So he could make a clean getaway.

What goes zzub, zzub,
A bee flying backwards.

What's the smallest
ant in the world?
An infant.

Man: "I want a hair-
cut, please."
Barber: "Certainly,
Sir. Which one?"

What's the
cannibal's favourite
restaurant called?
Man Alive.

Which two letters are
bad for your teeth?
D K.

There were two flies on
the wall, which one
was the bandit?
The one on the border.

Why did the lady
throw the clock out
of the window?
She wanted to see
time fly.

How do ghosts keep
their feet dry?
By wearing boots.

What kind of bandage
do people wear after
heart surgery?
Ticker tape.

What do you call a
jacket that's on fire?
A blazer.

What does the winner
lose in a race?
His breath.

What do you get if you cross a nun and a chick?
A pecking order.

How do you service
your pogo stick?
Give it a spring clean.

What do you get if you
cross a dog with a
stick insect?
An animal that will
fetch itself.

Why don't mummies
catch cold?
They're always well
wrapped up.

What has knobs on
and wobbles?
Jellyvision.

Why does a witch ride a broomstick at Hallowe'en?
So she can sweep the sky.

"Doctor, doctor, I've got double vision. How can I cure it?"
"Go around with one eye shut."

What's clever, sweet and travels by underground?
A tube of Smarties.

What's orange and sounds like a parrot?
Carrot.

What happened to the author that died?
He became a ghost writer.

How do chickens communicate?
By using fowl language.

Where should a twenty pound banana go?
On a diet.

"Knock. Knock!"
"Who's there?"
"Ken."
"Ken who?"
"Ken I come in?"

Why do elephants
have trunks?
Because they'd look
pretty stupid
with suitcases.

What do you find in a
wobbly pram?
A jelly baby.

Why shouldn't you tell a
secret to pigs?
Because they're squealers.

What do you call a
clock in space?
A lunar tick.

"Waiter, waiter, have
you got frog's legs?"
"No, Sir, I always walk
like this."

When is a blue book
not a blue book?
When it's read.

Which monster eats
faster than all the
other monsters?
The goblin.

What do you call a dinosaur at the North Pole?
Lost.

What do you get if you cross an elephant with a skunk?
A big stinker.

What makes an octopus a good fighter?
He's very well-armed.

What happens if you play tennis with a bad egg?
First it goes ping, then it goes pong.

What's a cheerful flea called?
A Hoptimist.

What kind of gum do bees chew?
Bumblegum.

What do you get if you cross a pig with a fir tree?
A pork-u-pine.

What kind of biscuit flies?
A plane biscuit.

What's always flying and never goes anywhere?
A flag.

Why did the nurse
creep silently past
the cupboard?
She didn't want to
wake the sleeping pills.

What happens if you
eat Christmas decorations?
You get tinselitis.

What sort of ball
doesn't bounce?
A snowball.

"Knock! Knock!"
"Who's there?"
"Isabel."
"Isabel who?"
"Isabel necessary on
a bicycle?"

What do you call a
dwarf novelist?
A short story writer.

What's the longest
night of the year?
A fortnight.

"Doctor, doctor, I've
got flat fee."
"Get a foot pump
then."

How did the idiot burn
his neck?
Ironing his shirt.

How did tap shoes get their name?
They fell in the sink.

Why don't ghosts make good magicians?
You can see right through their tricks.

What was Noah's occupation?
Preserving pears.

Why was the ghost arrested?
He didn't have a haunting licence.

What's the most important thing to remember in chemistry?
Never lick the spoon.

What do you get if you pour water down a rabbit hole?
Hot cross bunnies.

Teacher: "What's a robin?"
Pupil: "A bird that steals, miss."

Why are school cooks cruel?
Because they batter fish and beat eggs.

How do you spell 'mousetrap' using only three letters?
CAT.

What should you take if you're run down?
The number of the car that hit you.

"Knock! Knock!"
"Who's there?"
"Atch."
"Atch who?"
"Bless you!"

What do footballers and babies have in common?
They both dribble.

Why can't you pull a snake's leg?
Because he hasn't got one.

What do you get if you cross a burglar with a concrete mixer?
A hardened criminal.

"Doctor, doctor, I think I'm a clock."
"Well don't get too wound up about it."

Why do lions eat raw meat?
Because they don't know how to cook it.

What kind of lion never attacks people?
A dandelion.

Why did the ghost's trousers fall down?
Because he had no visible means of support.

Why did the pig cross the road?
Because it was the chicken's day off.

What's a python's favourite game?
Snakes and ladders.

"Doctor, doctor, I think I'm a witch."
"You'd better lie down for a spell."

What do you call a wizard from outer space?
A flying sorcerer.

What snakes are good at sums?
Adders.

What trees do fingers and thumbs grow on?
Palm trees.

Why did the egg go into the jungle?
He was an eggsplorer.

Roses are red,
Violets are blue,
I copied your exam paper,
And I failed too.

How does a vampire enter his house?
Through the bat flap.

What did stone age men like listening to?
Rock music.

What happens to a witch when she loses her temper?
She flies off the handle.

"Doctor, doctor, I think I'm a pack of cards."
"Sit down and I'll deal with you later."

Why did the orange stop rolling down the hill?
It ran out of juice.

What kind of cans are there in Mexico?
Mexicans.

How do hippos
play squash?
They jump on each other.

What is a gargoyle?
What ghosts take for a
sore throat.

What's the best
way to see a
flying saucer?
Trip up a waiter.

How does a tailor make
his trousers last?
He makes the jacket first.

What is a mermaid?
A deep-she fish.

What dog smells
of onions?
A hot dog.

Did you hear about
the man with
grease stains all
over his jacket?
He had a chip on
his shoulder.

What did one eye say
to the other eye?
Between you and me
something smells.

What followed
the dinosaur?
Its tail.

Did you hear about the
sick gnome?
He went to the elf centre.

What did the grape do when the
elephant sat on it?
It let out a little wine.

"Knock! Knock!"
"Who's there?"
"Juno."
"Juno who?"
"Do you know what time it is?"

What did the carpet
say to the floor?
I've got you covered.

What tree is always ill?
A sycamore.

What goes through
water and doesn't
get wet?
A shaft of sunlight.

What do you call a flea that
lives in an idiot's ear?
A space invader.

What capital city
cheats at exams?
Peking.

How can you tell if a
giant is under your bed?
Your nose touches
the ceiling.

Why is history the
sweetest lesson?
Because it's full
of dates.

Why was the Egyptian
girl worried?
Because her Daddy was
a Mummy.

What do you get if you cross a monster
with a cat?
A neighbourhood without dogs.

"Doctor, doctor, I
feel like a pin."
"I see your point."

Why did the skeleton go to
the party?
For a rattling good time.

What can a bottle of soda hold that a million men can't?
A bubble.

Why are skunks always arguing?
Because they like to raise a stink.

What do you call an American drawing?
A Yankee Doodle.

What did the spider say to the beetle?
Stop bugging me.

What cake wanted to rule the world?
Attila the Bun.

"Doctor, doctor, my wooden leg is giving me a lot of pain."
"Why's that?"
"My wife keeps hitting me over the head with it."

Why do koalas carry their babies on their backs?
They can't push prams up trees.

What do you call an Irish spider?
Paddy Long Legs.

What makes grass so
dangerous?
The blades.

What do you call a lady
who doesn't like butter?
Marge.

What do you get if
you cross a skunk
with a bear?
Winnie the Pooh.

How do you keep a
twit in suspense?
I'll tell you later.

Did you hear about the sheepdog who had her
puppies in the litter bin?
It said PLACE LITTER HERE on the front.

Why do bears wear
fur coats?
They'd look silly in
plastic macs.

What training do you
need to be a
rubbish collector?
None you pick it up as
you go along.

What did the dog say
to the skeleton?
I've got a bone to pick
with you.

What vegetables are
found in boats?
Leeks.

"Doctor, doctor, I feel
like a yo-yo."
"Sit down...sit
down...sit down."

What runs but has no legs?
Water.

What's the difference between a storm cloud
and a child that's been spanked?
One pours with rain and the other roars with pain.

Why do cats change their size?
Because they are let out at night and
taken in in the morning.

What do you call a
witch that can't
stop shaking?
A twitch.

When is cricket a crime?
When there's a hit and run.

What do you call a boy
on a pile of leaves?
Russell.

What is the opposite
of minimum?
Minidad.

What sort of
sweets do pigs
like best?
Swine gums.

What happens if
ducks fly upside
down?
They quack up.

Why do skeletons
drink so much milk?
Because it's good for
their bones.

What's served in
glasses and is difficult
to swallow?
A stiff drink.

Why do so many
people like fishing?
It's easy to get
hooked.

What happens when
plumbers die?
They go down the drain.

Why isn't it safe to sleep on trains? Because they run over sleepers.

"Doctor, doctor! I've only got 59 seconds to live!" "Wait a minute, please."

Can peas get married? Not if they're Batchelors.

Why is a football pitch always wet? Because the players are always dribbling.

Why did the skeleton run up the tree? Because the dog was after his bones.

What's another name for a sugar daddy? A lolly-pop.

What do mice have that no other animal has? Baby mice.

How do you know a snowman has been sleeping in your bed? You wake up wet.

What do you call
two robbers?
A pair of knickers.

"Doctor, doctor, I snore
so loudly I keep myself
awake. What can I do?"
"Sleep in another room."

How do you cure
a headache?
Put your head through
a window and the pane
will disappear.

What did the dentist
say when his wife
baked a cake?
"I'll do the filling, dear."

Why do witches do well
at school?
They're good at spelling.

What is a crocodile's
favourite game?
Snap.

Why did the man
take the duck back
to the pet shop?
It had a quack in it.

Why did the apple turnover?
Because it saw the jam roll.

"Doctor, doctor, I think I'm shrinking."
"Well, you'll have to be a little patient."

What has a bottom at the top?
A leg.

Why did the fish blush?
It saw the ocean's bottom.

What do monsters eat after having their teeth out?
The dentist.

There were two flies in the airing cupboard, which one was Scottish?
The one on the pipes.

"Doctor, doctor, I think I'm a fly!"
"Well buzz off then."

"Knock! knock!"
"Who's there?"
"Lettuce."
"Lettuce who?"
"Lettuce in while you read all the jokes."

Why did the woman fix her bed to the chandelier?
Because she was a light sleeper.

Why was the musician arrested?
For getting into treble.

What do geese eat?
Gooseberries.

What's the heaviest thing in a schoolboy's satchel?
A pencil - because it's full of lead.

Did you hear about the idiot who made his chickens drink hot water?
He thought they would lay hard boiled eggs.

"Mummy, mummy, the other kids keep saying I look like a werewolf."
"Be quite, dear, and go and comb your face."

Sid: "Who was that at the door?"
Ann: "A man with a wooden leg."
Sid: "Well, tell him to hop it."

What kind of beans do cannibals like best?
Human beans.

What do you call a woman with one leg shorter than the other?
Eileen.

Who never minds being interrupted in the middle of a sentence?
A convict.

"Knock! Knock!"
"Who's there?"
"Dana."
"Dana who?"
"Dana speak with your mouth full."

What relation is a doorstep to a doormat?
A stepfarther.

Why did the chewing gum cross the road?
It was stuck to the chicken's foot.

Why did the strawberries cry?
Because they were in a jam.

"Doctor, doctor, how can I stop myself from sleepwalking?"
"Sprinkle tacks on your bedroom floor."

Did you hear about the football team that were so bad the crowd changes were announced to the team?

What lives under the sea and carries people? An octobus.

What is a ghost's favourite dessert? Strawberries and scream.

Where do frogs put their coats? In a croak room.

Where do hamsters come from? Hamsterdam.

What goes into the water pink and comes out blue? A swimmer on a cold day.

What do traffic controllers like for tea? Traffic jam sandwiches.

What has two heads, three hands, two noses and five feet? A monster with spare parts.

When is a black dog not a black dog?
When it's a greyhound.

Did you hear about the village idiot buying some bird seed?
He said he wanted to grow some birds.

What's black and white, black and white, black and white?
A penguin rolling down a hill.

Why are vampires artistic?
They're good at drawing blood.

What has eight feet and sings?
The school quartet.

What kind of monster has the best hearing?
The eeriest.

What did one skeleton say to the other?
If we had any guts we'd get out of here.

What happened when the
dog swallowed a roll
of film?
Nothing serious developed.

What's a skeleton?
Bones with the
person off.

"Doctor, doctor,
I keep thinking I'm
a pair of curtains."
"Pull yourself
together, man."

Why is it difficult
to open up a
piano?
Because all the keys
are inside.

"What's the
difference between
a letterbox and an
elephant's bottom?"
"I don't know."
"Well, I hope your
mum never sends
you out to post
a letter."

Why is it bad to upset
a cannibal?
You'll end up in hot
water.

What do you get when
you cross a dog with
a chicken?
Pooched eggs.

What's the rudest food?
Sausages because they
spit at you.

How do you stop a
skunk from smelling?
Hold its nose.

Have you heard the one about the man who
bought a paper shop?
It blew away.

What do ducks watch on TV?
Duckumentaries.

I used to be a werewolf
but I'm howl right now.

What do golfers use in
China?
China tees.

What do you get
when you cross a
witch with an iceberg?
A cold spell.

What dress does
everyone have but
nobody wears?
An address.

63

Where do zombies go
for their jokes?
To crypt writers.

Why does a witch
ride on a broomstick?
Because a vacuum
cleaner is too heavy.

Why do ghosts like to
haunt tall buildings?
Because there's lots of
scarecases.

What do you call a
penguin in the
Sahara Desert?
Lost.

Did you hear about
the man who kept his
wife under his bed?
He thought she was
a little potty.

What tools do you
use in arithmetic?
Mulitpliers.

"Knock! Knock!"
"Who's there?"
"Isabel."
"Isabel who?"
"Isabel better than
all this knocking?"

Why did the one-eyed chicken cross the road?
To get to the Bird's Eye shop.

What room has no walls, no door and no ceiling?
A mushroom.

How do you make a reindeer fly?
Buy it an airline ticket.

What is enormous and has a red face?
A dinosaur with sunburn.

"Knock! knock!"
"Who's there?"
"Egbert."
"Egbert who?"
"Egbert no bacon."

If money doesn't grow on trees how come banks have so many branches?

What do you call a camel with three humps?
Humphrey.

What do you get if you cross a cat with a chemists?
Puss in Boots.

Did you hear about the man who sent his photograph to the Lonely Hearts Club? They sent it back and said they weren't that lonely.

What's the best day to fry eggs? Fryday.

When is water musical? When it's piping hot.

How do you save dumplings from drowning? Put them in gravy boats.

How do you knit a suit of armour? Use steel wool.

"Doctor, doctor, I keep thinking I'm a canary." "I can't tweet you. Go and see a vet."

Why do nuns walk on their heels? To save their souls.

What's a lazy rooster called? A cockle-doodle don't.

If you have a referee in football and an umpire in cricket, what do you have in bowls?
Goldfish.

What sits at the bottom of the sea and shakes?
A nervous wreck.

"Knock! Knock!"
"Who's there?"
"Genoa."
"Genoa who?"
"Genoa good teacher?"

Teacher: "Jones, you should have been here at nine o'clock."
Jones: "Why, what happened?"

What's grey, buzzes and eats cheese?
A mouse-quito.

What do you call a sick alligator?
An illigator.

What goes right up to a house but never goes in it?
A path.

What Elizabethan explorer
could stop bikes?
Sir Francis Brake.

What did the
Martian say to the
petrol pump?
Take your finger out
of your ear when I'm
talking to you.

What's brown and prickly
and squirts jam at you?
A hedgehog eating a
jam doughnut.

Why do you call your
dog camera?
Because he's
always snapping.

Man: "This coffee
tastes like mud."
Waitress: "It was only
ground
this morning."

If all the cars in Britain
were pink what would
you have?
A pink car-nation.

What's grey, has twelve
wheels and carries
a trunk?
An elephant, I lied about
the wheels.

What do you do if you find a monster in your bed?
Sleep somewhere else.

What did the man say when he saw a herd of elephants coming over the hill, wearing sunglasses?
Nothing. He didn't recognise them.

Teacher: "Who can tell me where the Andes are?"
Jimmy: "On the end of my armies."

What kind of lion never attacks people?
A dandelion.

Why do gorillas have big nostrils?
Have you seen the size of their fingers?

What do you call Postman Pat without a job?
Pat.

Where would you find a prehistoric cow?
In a moo-seum.

What did the two salt cellars say after they'd had a fight?
Shake.

What did the dirt say
to the rain?
If this keeps up my
name will be mud.

What kind of apes
talk a lot?
Blab-boons.

Vet: "I'm going to have
to put your
dog down."
Dog Owner: "Why?"
Vet: "He's so heavy
he's breaking my arm!"

What do you get if
you dial 666?
The Australian
police.

What bird lives
down a coal pit?
A mynah bird.

What do you call a
doctor who's
butterfingered?
A medicine dropper.

What do you call a nun
with a washing
machine on her head?
Sister-matic.

Why did the one-
handed man cross
the road?
To get to the second-
hand shop.

What's the difference between a shark and spaghetti?
A shark won't slip off the end of your fork.

What's the hottest letter in the alphabet?
B, because it makes oil boil.

What type of dog goes into the corner every time the bell rings?
A boxer.

What's Chinese and deadly dangerous?
Chop Sueycide.

What's grey and sits in a tree going "Hoots mon, hoots mon."
A Scottish owl.

Why did the skeleton go to the party?
For a rattling good time.

Why is Dracula so unpopular?
Because he's a pain in the neck.

Who said "Shiver me timbers!" on the ghost ship?
The skeleton crew.

"Knock! Knock!"
"Who's there?"
"Mary."
"Mary who?"
"Mary Christmas."

What girl would you
take fishing with you?
Annette.

What do ghosts have
for breakfast?
Dreaded wheat.

What sits in custard
looking cross?
Apple grumble.

Sam: "My dog's got no nose."
Ben: "How does he smell?"
Sam: "Awful!"

Why did the elephant
eat the candle?
He wanted a light snack.

What is the most
musical part of
a turkey?
The drumstick.

"Knock! Knock!"
"Who's there?"
"Robin."
"Robin who?"
"Robin your house!"

Why do eagles go
to church?
Because they are
birds of prey.

"Doctor, doctor I keep seeing double!"
"Please sit on the couch."
"Which one?"

What does a cat rest his head on?
A caterpillar.

What do you get from a
pampered cow?
Spoiled milk.

What creature is
useful in a car?
A windscreen viper.

"Doctor, doctor,
I'm boiling up!"
"Just simmer down."

What do you get if
you cross a vampire
with a mummy?
A flying bandage.

How did a farmer fix
his jeans?
With a cabbage patch.

"Doctor, doctor, I
feel like a
racehorse."
"Take one of these
every four laps."

What do fish take to
stay alive?
Vitamin sea.

Why do elephants
have wrinkles?
Because they don't
like ironing.

How did the telephones
get married?
In a double
ring ceremony.

"Knock! Knock!"
"Who's there?"
"Rufus."
"Rufus who?"
"Rufus leaking and
I'm getting wet!"

Why did the child
study in the aeroplane?
He wanted a higher
education.

"Knock! Knock!"
"Who's there?"
"Sarah."
"Sarah who?"
"Sarah doctor in
the house."

What language do they
speak in Cuba?
Cubic.

Where do dogs keep
their money?
Barklay's Bank.

How do you know when there's an
elephant in your bed?
It's got an E on its pyjamas.

Why did the clock get
sick?
It was run down.

What do you call a
cow eating grass in a
paddock?
A lawn mooer.

What do you call a foreign body in a chip pan?
An Unidentified Frying Object.

What happens if you eat yeast and shoe polish? You'll rise and shine in the morning.

What kind of ant is good at maths? An accountant.

Did I tell you the joke about the empty jar? There's nothing in it.

What car is like a sausage? An old banger.

What's black, crazy and sits in a tree? A raven lunatic.

Why did the giraffe wear black boots? His brown ones were at the menders.

What games do ants play with elephants? Squash.

What flies around your light at night and can bite off your head? A tiger moth.

"Doctor, doctor, I keep painting myself gold."
"Don't worry, it's a gilt complex."

Why was the broom late?
It overswept.

What should you call a bald teddy?
Fred bear.

How do you know if your cat's eaten a duckling?
She looks 'down in the mouth'.

When do mice need umbrellas?
When it's raining cats and dogs.

Why do giraffe's have long necks?
Have you smelt their feet?

What do lady ghosts put on their skin?
Vanishing cream.

What did the fireman's wife get for Christmas?
A ladder in her stocking.

Why did the dog chase its tail?
It was trying to make ends meet.

What is the most popular sentence at school?
I don't know.

What lights up the farmyard at night?
A battery hen.

What goes oink, clink, oink, clink?
A piggy bank.

What's the difference between a boring teacher and a boring book?
You can shut the book up.

What is the smelliest city in America?
Phew York.

What kind of dog wets the floor?
A poodle.

What cheese is made backwards?
Edam.

"Doctor, doctor, I've swallowed a spoon!"
"Just sit there quietly and don't stir."

How do you make a slow horse fast?
Don't feed it.

What looks like half a cat?
The other half.

What do you get if you cross a tiger with a snowman?
Frostbite.

What do vampires gamble with?
Stake money.

What gets bigger the more you take away?
A hole.

Why did the elephant wear sunglasses on the beach?
He didn't want to be recognised.

Why is history like a fruit cake?
Because it's full of dates.

What is small, pink, wrinkly and belongs to Granpa?
Grandma.

Which bus sailed over the sea?
Columbus.

"Waiter, do you serve crabs?"
"Sit down, Sir. We serve anybody."

If an apple a day keeps the doctor away, what does an onion do?
It keeps everyone away.

"Knock. Knock!"
"Who's there?"
"Abby."
"Abby who?"
"Abby stung me on the nose."

Did you hear the joke about the body snatchers?
I'd better not tell you – you might get carried away.

Where are famous monsters buried?
In Westmonster Abbey.

Why are feet like ancient tales?
Because they are leg-ends.

Did you hear about the two flies playing football in the saucer?
They were practising for the cup.

How do you keep cool at a football match?
Sit by a fan.

Mother: "Eat up your roast beef it's full of iron."
Danny: "No wonder it's tough."

What's noisy, runs around the field and sleeps all day?
A bulldozer.

Why did the bird cross the road?
Because the worm was on the other side.

What do you get if you cross a tiger with a kangaroo?
A stripey jumper.

What happened when the lion ate the comedian?
He felt funny.

What happened when the cat swallowed a penny?
There was money in the kitty.

"Nurse, nurse, I need to see a doctor!"
"Witch doctor?"
"No, a proper one."

What's the difference between a teacher and sweets?
People like sweets.

Did you hear about the monster who ate bits of metal every night?
It was his staple diet.

What schoolbooks help you get fit?
Exercise books.

What's the definition of a school report?
A poison pen letter from the headmaster.

What's striped and bouncy?
A tiger on a pogo stick.

Why didn't the skeleton play music in the church?
Because he had no organs.

What do you call a 100 year old ant?
An antique.

How do you hire a teddy bear?
Put him on stilts.

What is smaller than an ant's dinner?
An ant's mouth.

Why did the dog howl?
Because he was barking up the wrong tree.

What do you get when you cross a dive with a handstand?
A broken back.

"Doctor, doctor, I've got a split personality!"
"Well, you'd better both sit down then."

What subject are witches good at in school?
English! Because they're the tops at spelling.

What kind of dog hides
from frying pans?
A sausage dog.

What do you get if
you cross a leopard
with a watchdog?
A terrified postman.

What do
monsters eat
at sea?
Fish and ships.

How do you make a
glow worm happy?
Cut off his tail and
he'll be de-lighted.

What did the dog say
to the cat?
Woof, woof! (of course!)

How do sheep keep
warm in winter?
By central bleating.

What do you call a
robbery in Peking?
A Chinese takeaway.

When is water not water?
When it's dripping.

"Knock! knock!"
"Who's there?"
"Francis."
"Francis who?"
"Francis across the English Channel."

What's bright blue and weighs four tonnes?
An elephant holding its breath.

How do you make scotch eggs?
Feed your chicken whisky.

What do you call a Scottish parrot?
A Macaw!

Why is a sofa like a roast chicken?
Because they're both full of stuffing!

What's full of holes but can hold water?
A sponge.

How do you get a cut-price parrot?
Plant bird seed!

What's the difference between a tiger and a lion?
A tiger has the mane part missing.

"Doctor, doctor"
"I think I'm a snail!"
"Don't worry we'll soon
have you out of your shell."

What do owls sing
when it is raining?
"Too wet to woo!"

What language do
twins speak
in Holland?
Double Dutch.

"Knock! Knock!"
"Who's there?"
"Arthur."
"Arthur who?"
"Arthur any
biscuits?"

What kind of birds do
you usually find
locked up?
Jail-birds!

What do you call a man
floating on a raft in the sea?
Bob.

What happened to
the leopard who
took a bath three
times a day?
He was spotless.

"Doctor, doctor I keep
thinking I'm a nit!"
"Will you get out of my hair?"

What is a puppy's
life like?
Ruff.

What is a polygon?
A dead parrot.

"Doctor, doctor I think I'm an adder!"
"Great, can you help me with my
accounts then please?"

What swings from a tree
in a suit and a tie?
A branch manager.

What were Tarzan's
last words?
Who greased this vine?

"Doctor, doctor I feel
like an apple."
"We must get to the
core of this!"

What do you get if
you cross a glow
worm with a python?
A twenty foot
strip light.

Why is life like a shower?
One wrong turn and you're
in hot water.

"Doctor, doctor I
think I'm a butterfly."
"Will you say what you
mean and stop flitting
about!"

What happened when
the Ice Monster fell out
with the Zombie?
He gave him the
cold shoulder.

What do snowmen
wear on their heads?
Ice caps.

If Ireland fell into the
sea which part
would float?
Cork.

Who went into the
tiger's lair and came
out alive?
The tiger.

What's another word
for tears?
Glumdrops.

Where do birds meet
for coffee?
In a nest-cafe!

How does a bird with a broken wing manage to land safely?
With a sparrowchute!

What unlocks a Turkish house?
A turkey.

"Knock! Knock!"
"Who's there?"
"Snow."
"Snow who?"
"Snow good asking me."

What do you call a dinosaur with one eye?
Doyouthinkhesaurus.

What do you call a very rude bird?
A mockingbird!

What do you call a dinosaur with no eyes?
Iknoweneversawus.

What do you get if you cross a Scottish legend and a bad egg?
The Loch Ness Pongster.

Who invented the first plane that couldn't fly?
The Wrong brothers.

"Knock! Knock!"
"Who's there?"
"Affro."
"Affro who?"
"Affroed my ball into your garden."

What did the curtain say to the other curtain?
"Well, I'll be hanged."

What happened when the owl lost his voice?
He didn't give a hoot!

What do you get if you cross a zombie with a boy scout?
A creature that scares old ladies across the road.

What's the best way to avoid being troubled by biting insects?
Don't bite any.

What do you get if you cross a woodpecker with a carrier pigeon?
A bird who knocks before delivering its message!

What do you give short elves?
Elf-raising flour.

What do baby swans
dance to?
Cygnet-ure-tunes!

Did you hear about
the burglar who fell
in the cement mixer?
Now he's a
hardened criminal.

Did you hear about the
dentist who became a
brain surgeon?
His drill slipped.

Mary had a bionic cow,
It lived on safety pins,
Every time she milked that cow,
The milk came out in tins.

What's the easiest way
to make a banana split?
Cut it in half.

How can you see stars
during the daytime?
Hit yourself on the head.

What did the 'just married' spiders call their new home?
Newlywebs.

"Knock! Knock!"
"Who's there?"
"Cook."
"Cook who?"
"That's the first one I've heard this year."

"Waiter, waiter, I'm in a hurry! Will my pancake be long?"
"No, it will be round, Sir!"

How can you tell when it's rabbit pie for dinner?
It has hares in it.

What do you mean by telling everyone that I'm an idiot?
Sorry, I didn't know that it was meant to be a secret.

What happened to Ray when he met the man-eating monster?
He became ex-Ray.

Why was the cannibal expelled from school?
Because he kept buttering up the teachers.

How do you catch
a squirrel?
Climb up a tree and act
like a nut.

"I have two noses, three
eyes and only one ear.
What am I?"
"Very ugly!"

What's as light as a feather
but harder to hold?
Your breath.

How did the Vikings
communicate with
each other?
By Norse code.

"Knock. Knock!"
"Who's there?"
"A lady with a pram."
"Tell her to push off!"

Why are piano's
so noble?
Because they are
either upright
or grand.

"Waiter, what do you
suggest for a
quick snack?"
"Runner beans, sir."

93

What did one flea say to
the other flea?
Shall we walk or take a cat?

Why are
porpoises clever?
They swim around
in schools.

What did the
mouse say when it
lost its front teeth?
Hard cheese.

When do swimming
trunks go ding dong?
When you wring
them out.

What did the carpet
say to the desk?
I can see your
drawers.

What do you call two
witches that share a
broomstick?
Broom-mates.

What is a skeleton?
Someone who went
on a diet and forgot
to say "when".

What's the best butter in
the world?
A goat.

94

Where did Sir
Lancelot study?
In knight school.

What coat do you put on
only when it's wet?
A coat of paint.

How do you make a Swiss roll?
Lie him on his side and push him down the hill.

What is a falsehood?
A fake hat.

Why are
Martians green?
Because they forgot
to take their
travel-sickness tablets.

How do young
spooks prefer
their eggs?
Terrifried.

What do you call
an area where
ghosts live?
A terrortory.

Why were the witches on strike?
They wanted sweeping reforms.

What do ghosts wear if they're short-sighted?
Spooktacles.

What do you call a bumble bee with a quiet buzz?
A mumble bee.

What sort of ball doesn't bounce?
A snowball.

What do you call a flying skunk?
A smellacopter.

What part of fish do we eat that it actually doesn't have?
Fish fingers.

What is the correct name for a water otter?
A kettle.

"Doctor, doctor, I keep thinking I'm a caterpillar."
"Don't worry you'll soon change."

"Who was that at the door?"
"A man with a drum."
"Tell him to beat it!"

How does a ghoul
start a letter?
Tomb it may concern.

What goes hum-choo,
hum choo?
A bee with a cold!

Why did the cat join the Red Cross?
Because she wanted to be a first-aid kit!

"Doctor, doctor my
husband smells like
fish."
Poor sole!

Why did the bird cry?
Because it was a
bluebird.

How long do chickens work?
Around the cluck!

Where do Martians
drink beer?
At a mars bar.

"Doctor, doctor I've lost my
memory."
"When did this happen?"
"When did what happen?"

"Knock! Knock!"
"Who's there?"
"Hammond."
"Hammond who?"
"Hammond eggs."

What do you get if
you cross King Kong
with a budgie?
A messy cage.

What's black,
yellow and
covered in
blackberries?
A bramble bee!

Why was the cat
so small?
Because it only drank
condensed milk.

Why did the turtle
cross the road?
To go to the Shell
station.

What happened to the
man who swallowed
a doorknob?
It turned his stomach.

What do you get when a chicken
lays an egg on top of a barn?
An eggroll!

What kind of
dog chases
anything red?
A bull dog!

What is the definition of a goose?
An animal that grows down as it grows up!

Where do fish go to
borrow money?
To a loan shark!

"Doctor, doctor will this
ointment clear up
my spots?"
"I never make
rash promises!"

What do ghosts dance to?
Soul music!

How do Welsh people
eat cheese?
Caerphilly!

Why doesn't the sea
spill over the earth?
Because it's tied!

What is the most
slippery country in
the world?
Greece!

What is 'out of bounds'?
An exhausted kangaroo!

What is hail?
Hard boiled rain!

Who was the most
powerful cat
in China?
Chairman Miaow!

Why did the cat cross
the road?
It was the chicken's
day off!

"Doctor, doctor what
did the x-ray of my
head show?"
"Absolutely nothing!"

"Doctor, doctor
everyone thinks I'm
a liar."
"I can't believe that!"

"Knock. Knock!"
"Who's there?"
"Phillipa."
"Phillipa who?"
"Phillipa bath,
I'm dirty."

What do you get if you
cross an eagle with
a skunk?
A bird that stinks to
high heaven.

What is a baby bee?
A little humbug!

Why did the reindeer
laze in the sun?
Because he wanted to
tan his hide.

Did you hear about
the idiot karate
champion that joined
the army?
The first time he
saluted he nearly
killed himself.

What is a baby elephant after he is
five weeks old?
Six weeks old!

"Doctor, doctor I'm
having trouble with my
breathing."
"I'll give you something
that will soon put a
stop to that!"

"Knock. Knock!"
"Who's there?"
"Tish."
"Tish who?"
"Bless you."

What do you get if you cross a parrot
with an elephant?
An animal that tells you everything that it
remembers!

Why do the elephants
have short tails?
Because they can't
remember long stories!

"Doctor, doctor I'm
so ugly what can I do
about it?"
"Hire yourself out for
Halloween parties!"

Why are
fried onions like a
photocopying machine?
They keep
repeating themselves.

Why don't centipedes
play football?
Because by the time
they've got their boots
on it's time to go home.

What kind of ghosts
haunt hospitals?
Surgical spirits.

What do you give a
pony with a cold?
Cough Stirrup!

102

What do you call a pig
with no clothes on?
Streaky bacon!

What animal always goes
to bed with its shoes on?
A horse!

Doctor, doctor I think
I'm a moth.
Get out of the way,
you're in my light!

Why was Cinderella
thrown out of the
school's netball team?
Because she kept
running away from
the ball.

"Doctor, doctor I keep
seeing an insect
spinning around."
"Don't worry, it's just
a bug that's
going around!"

Why is a fish easy
to weigh?
Because it has its
own scales!

What do you get if
you try to take a
ghost's photograph?
Transparencies.

Why is the graveyard
such a noisy place?
Because of all
the coffin.

What do you get if
you cross a ghost with
a packet of crisps?
Snacks that go crunch
in the night.

Why are dolphins cleverer than humans?
Within three hours they can train a man to stand
at the side of a pool and feed them fish!

What makes the Tower
of Pisa lean?.
It doesn't eat much

How do you get rid
of varnish?
Take away the R.

"Doctor, doctor I keep
getting pains in the eye
when I drink coffee."
"Have you tried taking
the spoon out?"

Who was the best
actor in the bible?
Samson, he brought
the house down!

Did you hear about the little boy who was named after his father?
They called him Dad.

"Waiter, waiter, I don't like the flies in here."
"Well, come back tomorrow, we'll have new ones by then."

What is an archaeologist?
Someone whose career is in ruins!

What lies on the ground 100 feet in the air and smells?
A dead centipede.

Did you hear about the mad scientist who put dynamite in his fridge?
They say it blew his cool!

Why did the idiot have his sundial floodlit?
So he could tell the time at night!

Why didn't the banana snore?
Because he was afraid to wake up the rest of the bunch.

Why are fish boots the warmest ones to wear?
Because they have electric 'eels!

"Doctor, doctor I think I'm a rubber band."
"Why don't you stretch yourself out on the couch there and tell me all about it!"

What exams do farmers take?
Hay levels.

What do you call a bad lion tamer?
Claude Bottom.

Why is six scared of seven?
Because 7- 8- 9.

How does the moon cut his hair?
E-clipse it.

What do you get if Batman and Robin get smashed by a steam roller?
Flatman and Ribbon.

When is a car not a car?
When it turns into a garage.

What do sheep do on
sunny days?
Have a baa-baa cue.

What do they call kittens
in the Wild West?
Posse cats.

Who was the Black Prince?
The son of Old King Cole.

What do bees chew?
Bumble gum.

What do you call a dog in
jeans and a sweater?
A plain clothes police dog!

What is the most
musical part of
a turkey?
The drumstick.

Did you hear about the
really stupid woodworm?
It was found dead in
a housebrick.

107

Why did the boy put sugar on his pillow?
So he could have sweet dreams.

Where do astronauts keep their sandwiches?
In a launch box.

"Waiter, waiter, there's a maggot in my salad!"
"Don't worry, Sir. It won't live long in that stuff!"

What do you get if you cross a worm with a young goat?
A dirty kid.

What did the skunk say when the wind changed?
"It's all coming back to me now."

What sort of animal is a slug?
A snail with a housing problem.

Man: (tucking into sandwich): "This bread is nice and warm."
Wife: "So it should be, the cat's been sitting on it all day."

108

What has one horn and
gives fresh milk?
A milk truck.

Why was the
centipede late?
Because she was
playing this little piggy
with her baby.

"Doctor, doctor, I think
I'm a billiard ball."
"Sorry, you'll have to go
to the end of the queue."

Did you hear about the plastic surgeon?
He sat in front of the fire and melted.

If cows get milked
what do goats get?
Butted.

What do you call a
multi-storey pig pen?
A sty-scraper.

What skin complaint
comes from London?
Hackney.

"Doctor, doctor, I keep
thinking I'm a mosquito."
"Go away, sucker!"

109

What did the hypochondriac have written on his tomb?
I TOLD YOU I WAS ILL.

What's the wettest animal?
A reindeer.

How do you catch a vampire fish?
With blood worms.

What do you get if you cross a dog and a skunk?
Rid of the dog!

What do you get if you cross a vampire with a rose?
A flower that goes for your throat when you sniff it.

Roses are red,
Violets are pink,
There's an octopus in the bath,
So I'll have wash in the sink!

"Doctor, doctor, three beer kegs have just fallen on me."
"Don't worry, it was light ale."

"Doctor, doctor, I've broken my arm in two places."
"Well, don't go back there again."

Did you hear about the tailor who made his trousers from sun-blind material?
Every time the sun came out, his trousers rolled down.

Why is a Christmas tree like a bad knitter?
They both drop their needles.

What do you call a flying policeman?
A helicopper.

What animal drives a motor car?
A road hog.

What is red, sweet and bites people in the neck?
A Jampire!

111

What kind of cow wears a jumper?
A jersey.

What does an accountant at the police station do?
Count the coppers.

What did the zombie get a medal for?
Deadication.

Where do baby fish go?
To plaice-school.

What do you get if you cross a skeleton with peanut butter?
Extra crunchy peanut butter.

Why do seagulls live by the sea?
Because if they lived by the bay they'd be bagels.

Which is the best hand to write with?
Neither, it's best to write with a pen.

How can you stop a
cold going to
your chest?
Tie a knot in your neck.

What was King Arthur's
court famous for?
Its knight life.

What can lizards do
that snakes can't do?
Stretch their legs.

Teacher: "Which
family does the
octopus belong to?"
Pupil: "No one in our
street, miss."

What would happen if tarantulas
were as big as horses?
If one bit you you could ride it to hospital.

"Doctor, doctor, my baby's
just swallowed a watch."
"Give it some Epsom salts,
that should help it pass
the time."

Who was the skeleton
in the cupboard?
The winner of last
year's hide and seek.

113

"Knock! Knock!"
"Whose there?"
"Snow."
"Snow who?"
"Snow good asking me."

A lady fell down the well, how did she get out?
She had a ladder in her tights.

Doctor: "You've got a nasty chill, you must avoid draughts for a week or two."
Patient: "Can I play ludo instead?"

Where would a sleepy man post a letter?
In a pillow-box.

What stars go to jail?
Shooting stars.

How do you join Dracula's club?
Send in your name, address and blood group.

What do you get if you cross a bee with a skunk?
Something that stings and smells.

114

Where does a sick
ship go?
To the dock.

What rooms don't
skeletons like?
Living rooms.

Did you hear about the man who stole
a lorry load of prunes?
He's been on the run for a week.

Why did the hazelnut
go out with a prune?
Because he couldn't
find a date.

Why did the doll
blush?
Because she saw the
teddy bear.

"Doctor, doctor, I
think I'm a banana."
"Well slip over there
and peel off
your clothes."

"Knock! Knock!"
"Who's there?"
"Corah."
"Corah who?"
"Corah wish I had a
front door like this!"

115

"Doctor, doctor, I feel like a sheep."
"That's baaaa-d!"

"Knock! Knock!"
"Who's there?"
"Al."
"Al who?"
"Al give you a kiss if you open the door!"

Patient: "Well, Doctor, how do I stand?"
Doctor: "I don't know, it's a miracle."

What's green, has four legs and two trunks?
Two seasick tourists.

What goes at 300kph on a washing line?
Honda pants.

When is an operation funny?
When it leaves the patient in stitches.

Why did the man put a net over his head?
Because he wanted to catch his breath.

Ten cats were in a boat and one jumped out. How many were left? None, they were all copycats.

What is a female monster's favourite saying? Demon's are a girl's best friend.

Little sausage dog,
Crossing the street,
Here comes a motor car,
Now it's sausage meat.

I'm not saying our teacher's fat but every time he falls over he rocks himself to sleep trying to get back up.

How many witches can you fit in an empty coffin? One. After that it isn't empty any more.

What do you get when you cross an ocean with a comedian? Waves of laughter.

What is a myth? A female moth.

Teacher: "Why do you always fail your exams?"
Pupil: "Because I keep getting the wrong exam paper."

What did the policeman say when he saw three angels?
"Halo, halo, halo!"

Where do policemen live?
999 Letsbe Avenue.

Which fruit is always on a coin?
A date.

What do you do if you find a trumpet growing in your garden?
Root-it-oot.

What kind of shoes are made out of banana skins?
Slippers.

"Doctor, doctor, I feel like an apple."
"It's okay, I won't bite you."

Doctor: You really have acute hearing.
Patient: Thank you, it's real gold, you know.

Do robots have brothers?
No, but they have tran-sisters.

What's brown and sneaks around the kitchen?
Mince spies.

What did Batman give Robin for breakfast?
Worms.

What do you call a wooden king?
A ruler.

What do you call a dog with no legs?
You can call it what you want, it still won't come.

What bird is mechanical?
The crane.

Why do nuns walk on their heels?
To save their soles.

How did the police find Quasimodo?
They followed a hunch.

Why did the man take
a ladder to the party?
Because the drinks
were on the house.

What do you get
if you cross a frog
with a dog?
A croaker spaniel.

What did the stick
insect say to his
friend?
Stick around.

Why can't you play
cards in the jungle?
There are too
many cheetahs.

What's the first thing
a bat learns at
school?
The alphabat.

"Knock! Knock!"
"Who's there?"
"Stan."
"Stan who?"
"Stan back, I'm
breaking the
door down."

What goes "HA, HA BONK!"
A man laughing his head off.

Who speaks at a ghost's
conference?
A spooksman.

What do you get if you cross a ghost and a senior policeman?
A chief inspectre.

What do you get if you cross Dracula with Sir Lancelot?
A bite in shining armour.

Mother: "What did you learn in school today?"
Susie: "Not enough, I have to go back tomorrow."

Did you hear the joke about the empty house?
There was nothing in it.

What was written on the metal monster's gravestone?
Rust in Peace.

Was Dracula ever married?
No, he was a bat-chiller.

Bob: "I like your Easter tie?"
Stan: "Why do you call it my Easter tie?"
Bob: "It's got egg on it."

"Doctor, doctor, I think I'm a dog."
"Sit down please."
"Oh no, I'm not allowed on the furniture."

What did the man catch when he went fly-fishing?
A 20-tonne bluebottle.

Teacher: "How do you spell wrong?"
Anna: "R-o-n-g."
Teacher: "That's wrong."
Anna: "That's what you asked for, isn't it?"

"Waiter, what's wrong with this fish?"
"Long time, no sea, sir."

Angry Father: "Who broke the window?"
Tommy: "Ben, did Dad. He ducked when I threw the stone at him."

If twenty dogs run after one dog, what time is it?
Twenty after one.

Why did the lazy man get a job in a bakery?
Because he wanted a good loaf.

What do you get when you cross an apple with a Christmas tree?
A pine-apple.

Where does a general keep his armies?
Up his sleevies.

What do you get if you cross a chicken with a cow?
Roast beef.

Why does an ostrich have such a long neck?
Because its head is so far from its body.

What's yellow and sniffs?
A banana with a bad cold.

"Doctor, doctor, I think I need glasses."
"You certainly do, Sir. This is a fish and chip shop"

Why did the man jump up and down?
He'd forgotten to shake his medicine.

What is a mushroom?
The school dining hall.

Mary had a little lamb,
He had a touch of colic,
She gave him brandy
twice a day,
And now he's alcoholic!

Why did the man put
corn in his shoes?
Because he had
pigeon toes.

How do you make a
reindeer stew?
Make it wait for hours.

What do you call an
ant with frog's legs?
An antiphibian.

Why did the ant elope?
Nobody gnu.

"Doctor, doctor, I think
I'm turning into a frog."
"You're just playing too
much croquet."

"Doctor, doctor, I
keep thinking I'm a
woodworm."
"How boring for you."

"Doctor, doctor, I
swallowed a bone."
"Are you choking?"
"No, I really did."

Why did the elephant put his trunk across the path?
To trip up the ants.

What's a French cat's favourite pudding?
Chocolate mousse.

What ant can you crayon with?
A crayant.

What did the cat say when he lost all his money?
"I'm paw."

"Doctor, doctor, I dream there's monsters under my bed. What can I do?"
"Saw the legs off your bed."

How many ants are needed to fill an apartment?
Ten-ants.

"Doctor, doctor, I keep thinking I'm an electric eel."
"How shocking."

Why is it funny to see a boy run a mile?
Because he really moves two feet.

Why did the liquorice
go jogging?
Because it was a
liquorice all-sport.

What two things
can't you have for
breakfast?
Lunch and dinner?

Why was the crab
arrested?
It kept pinching things.

Why don't
midfielders like
going on planes?
Because they might
be put on the wings.

Did you hear about the
robbers who stole a
calendar?
They got six months each.

Father: "What position
do you play in the school
football team?"
Son: "The games
teacher said I'm the
main drawback."

"Knock! Knock!"
"Who's there?"
"Sam."
"Sam who?"
"Sam Francisco,
here I come!"

What did one wall say to the other wall?
"I'll meet you at the corner."

"Knock! Knock!"
"Who's there?"
"Anna."
"Anna who?"
"Annanother thing, how long do I have to keep knocking!"

Did you hear about the girl who dreamed she was eating a giant marshmallow?
When she woke up in the morning her pillow was gone.

What wears shoes but has no feet?
A pavement.

What's got two legs, two arms and is good on a dark night?
A light-headed man.

"Knock! knock!"
"Who's there?"
"Felix."
"Felix who?"
"Felix my lolly I'll punch him on the nose."

What do you get if you cross a rocket with a kangaroo?
A space shuttle that makes short hops.

127

Have you ever seen a duchess?
Yes, it's the same as an English 's'!

"Is this a second hand shop?"
"Yes, Sir."
"Good. Can you fit one on my watch please."

What is Indian snow like?
Apache here, apache there.

Why did the angel lose her job?
She had harp failure.

Did you hear about the mad scientist who invented a gas that could burn through anything?
Now he's trying to invent something to hold it in.

"Knock! Knock!"
"Who's there?"
"Ammonia."
"Ammonia who?"
"Ammonia little girl and I can't reach the door."

Why does it snow in winter?
Because the snow would melt in summer.

What is the most
expensive dog?
A deerhound

What is the
warmest tree?
A fir tree.

What happens if you
cross a turkey with
an octopus?
Everyone gets a leg
at Christmas.

How do you stop a dog
from digging holes in
your garden?
Hide his spade.

What do misers do
in cold weather?
Sit around a candle.

What do misers do in
very cold weather?
Light it!

Where do all good
turkeys go when they die?
To oven.

Why is the letter 'r'
like Christmas?
It comes at the end
of December.

What do a dog and a tree
have in common?
Bark.

"Waiter, waiter, you've got your thumb on my steak!" "I know, Sir, I don't want it to fall on the floor again."

What does a deaf fisherman need?
A herring aid.

"Knock! Knock!"
"Who's there?"
"Irish stew."
"Irish stew who?"
"Irish stew in the name of the law."

"Waiter, this chicken has dots on it."
"It's okay, Sir, it's only chicken pox."

When is a boat like a heap of snow?
When it comes a-drift.

What do you call someone who makes half size models of fish?
A scale modeller.

What do you call a chocolate that teases small animals?
A mole-teaser.

What do you call a football match played by chimney sweeps?
Sootball.

130

What do you call a
very fast horse?
A gee gee whizz.

What do you call a
musical instrument that
is played by two teams
of twenty people?
A piano forte.

Why did the
football pitch end up
as a triangle?
Somebody took a corner.

Why was
the roadrunner
hopping mad?
He ran out of roads.

What do you get if you type www.(and then
the whole alphabet) into your computer?
A sore finger.

Dad: "You're sitting for
hours in front of that
computer. Have you
had your eyes
checked?"
Son: "No, they've
always been green."

What usually happens
after a monster lights
the candles on his
birthday cake?
Someone sends for the
fire brigade.

Why did the tennis player have his hands over his ears?
He couldn't stand the racket.

Why is an elevator like a car?
It can give you a lift.

Why was the trapeze artist like a pet bird?
He was always flying from swing to swing.

Why would the luggage handler make a good detective?
He hardly ever loses a case.

Why did nobody like the tell-tale witch?
She was a snitch.

Why was the witch at the seashore tasty?
She was a sand-witch.

What do you call a pig who lives in a hedge?
A hedgehog.

Why are cats paws so soft?
So the mice don't hear them creeping up.

What do you get if you cross a psychic with a TV?
Tele-vision.

Why was the tree too noisy?
Because of its bark.

Girl: "What sort of plant do you have in your hand?"
Other girl: "A palm tree."

What do you call someone who never stops drinking cocoa?
A coco-nut.

Why were the stick insects such great friends?
They were always sticking up for each other at school.

Why was the cat upset?
He was in a cat-flap.

Why is a cat cleaner than a dog?
It washes itself everyday.

What did the fisherman use as a bookmark?
A flat fish - to mark the plaice.

Why was the ghost shy?
He didn't want to make a spectre of himself.

Why were the ghost's teeth horrible?
He was frightened to go to the dentist.

What's the difference between lightning and electricity?
Lightning is free of charge.

Why couldn't the spaceman land on the moon?
It was already full.

What do pelicans eat?
Anything that fits the bill.

What sea creature is good at adding?
An octoplus.

What time is it when your watch strikes thirteen?
Time to get a new watch.

When is the moon heaviest?
When it's full.

What does a duck wear when it dresses up?
A duxedo.

What time do most people go to the dentist?
Tooth-hurty.

What do children make that adults can't see?
A lot of noise.

How can you guarantee good weather when you go to the beach?
Go on a Sunday.

How can you tell the difference between a tin of tomato soup and a tin of chicken soup?
Always read the label.

What happened to the wolf who was put in the washing machine?
He became a wash and werewolf.

What was the Mexican weather report?
Chilli today, hot tamale.

What word if pronounced right is wrong but if pronounced wrong is right?
Wrong.

Why were the lookalike witches confusing?
It was difficult to tell witch was witch.

How do you know if a
boat is affectionate?
It hugs the coast.

Why are sheep boring?
They talk constantly -
blah, blah, blah.

What did the
Headmaster do when
he saw the school's
gas bill?
He exploded.

Did you hear about
the woman who lost
her budgie?
She called the
flying squad!

How do students sail
on the sea?
On scholarships.

What did the boy
squirrel say to the
girl squirrel?
"I'm nuts about you."

What's the difference
between a sick monster
and seven days?
One is a weak one and
the other one week!

Did you hear about the
ghost that kept
making mistakes?
It made 'boo-boos!'

Did you hear about the woman who put her bed in a fire? She wanted to sleep like a log!

Did you hear about the mattress robbery? The police 'sprang' into action!

Did you hear about the comedian's motorbike? It was a Yama-ha-ha!

Where do astronauts park their spaceships? At parking meteors!

What do you get if you cross a monster and a chicken? Free strange eggs!

Did you hear about the man who crossed a fish and bad breath? He got halibut-osis.

Did you hear about the tree in the maths class? It grew square roots.

What do you get if you cross a footballer with a fish? A goalkipper!

Where do sheep go
on holiday?
To Ramsgate!

What came after
the dinosaurs?
Their tails!

Did you hear about
the cat that ate
a duck?
It turned into a duck-
filled-fatty-puss!

Why didn't the
gnome go to work?
He stayed at home
for 'elf' reasons!

What did the duck
said to the waiter?
"Why have you put this
lunch on my bill?"

Did you hear about the
astronomer who hit
his head?
He saw stars!

Did you hear about the
broom hand signal?
It was a sweeping gesture!

Did you hear about the
man who crossed a dog
with a game of football?
He played spot-the-ball!

What is yellow and very dangerous?
Shark-infested custard!

Why did the spider buy a computer?
He wanted to make a web page!

Teacher: "What's the Equator?"
Pupil: "It's an imaginary lion running around the Earth!"

What is a cleaner's favourite fairy tale?
Sweeping Beauty!

What is a traffic warden's favourite cartoon?
Aladdin and the Magic Clamp!

What do you get if you cross a sports reporter with a vegetable?
A common tater!

Did you hear about the man who crossed a wireless with a hairdresser?
He got radio waves!

What happens when authors die?
They become ghost writers!

What is a skeleton's
favourite shellfish?
Mussels!

Which is the longest
piece of furniture
at school?
The multiplication table!

What did the necklace
say to the hat?
"You go on ahead, I'll
just hang around!"

What did the chocolate
say to the lollipop?
"Hello sucker!"

What did Charles I
say before he
was executed?
"Can I go for a walk
around the block?"

What did the jack say
to the car?
"Want a lift?"

What is a composer's favourite party game?
Haydn seek!

What happened after
Beethoven died?
He decomposed!

What is a traffic
policeman's favourite
sandwich filling?
Traffic jam!

What happens when a skunk dies? It's ex-stinked!

Did you hear about the insect film director? They call him Steven Spielbug!

Did you hear about the man who crossed a cocoa bean with an elk? He got chocolate mousse!

What do you get if you cross a lawn with a kangaroo? A grasshopper!

What was the booby prize at the nudist beach ball competition? A clothes brush!

What do you call a woman with a bunch of holly on her head? Carol!

Did you hear about the boy who didn't like decimals? He couldn't see the point!

What do you get if you cross a big dog with an oak tree? A very loud bark!

What do you call a
baby whale?
A little squirt!

Why are surgeon's
so funny?
They have everyone
in stitches!

Did you hear about
the stupid
ventriloquist?
He only performed on
the radio!

Did you hear about
the dinner lady with
blancmange on
her head?
She was in the pink!

Why is it good to have
an octopus with you if
you go into battle?
They are well armed!

Did you hear about the
stupid inventor?
He invented colour radio!

What happened when
the man ate his
whiskers?
He got a beard belly!

Did you hear about
the man with a two
foot beard?
He walks on his chin!

Did you hear the rumour about the fish fighting outside a chip shop?
It's a load of old codswallop!

What happened when the chicken fell in the cement mixer?
It became a bricklayer!

What happened when the duck lost its voice?
It had to visit the quack!

What happened when the wheel was invented?
It caused a revolution!

Did you hear about the constipated mathematician?
He worked it out with a pencil!

What do you call a pirate who makes lots of mistakes?
Wrong John Silver!

Why did the greedy man want to work in a bank?
He'd been told there was a lot of money in it!

Why did the telephone engineer leave his job?
It was driving him up the pole!

Who is the patron
saint of school
playgrounds?
St Francis of a see-saw!

What did the dentist
say to the pie maker?
"Can I do the fillings?"

What did the
undertaker say to his
girlfriend?
"Em balmy about you!"

Did you hear about the
nervous man who ate
caterpillars?
He developed butterflies
in his stomach!

Did you hear about the
boy who wanted
to be a bus?
Nobody stood in his way!

Why did the postman
get the sack?
To put his letters in!

Did you hear about the
giraffe that was slow
to apologise?
It took him a long time
to swallow his pride!

Why did the ram
run over the cliff?
He didn't see the
'ewe' turn!

What do you call a woman with a cat on her head?
Kitty!

Which newspaper do cows read?
The Daily Moos.

Why was the doctor bad-tempered?
Because he had no patience!

What has a big horn and is very dangerous?
A motor car!

When are hilltops most crowded?
In 'peak' season!

What do you call a ghost that haunts a chat show host?
Phantom of the 'Oprah'!

Did you hear about the miserable dentist?
He always looked down in the mouth!

What do you call a sick crocodile?
An illigator!

Why did the books get out of the school bag?
They were exercise books!

What do you get when
you cross a coward
with a black bird?
A scarecrow!

How do bees get
to school?
By school buzz!

How do teachers
dress in January?
Quickly!

"Doctor, doctor, I feel
like I'm in some
boiled fruit!"
"You are in a jam!"

What is the craziest
country of all?
Mad-agascar!

First man: "I always
get new clothes
when I'm down in
the dumps!"
Second man: "I
wondered where!"

Did you hear about
the wizard's horse?
It turned into a barn!

What has six eyes and still
can't see anything at all?
Three blind mice!

What do you call a man who steals bacon?
A hamburglar!

Why did the fortune-teller pack her job in? Because she could see no future in it!

Why is a broken machine like a failed doctor?
They don't operate!

What do you call the Moon after a huge feast?
A full Moon!

What do you get when you cross a bee with meat in a bun?
A humburger!

What do you call an Arabian ruler with lots of cows?
A milk sheik!

"Doctor, doctor, I think I'm a television programme, a television programme!"
"Don't repeat yourself!"

At what time of day was Adam created?
A little before Eve!

What do you get after it has been taken?
Your photo!

Which musicians can you never trust?
Fiddlers!

What do you call a man on the floor that lifts up a car?
Jack!

What do you get when you cross a cow with a theme park ride?
A milk shake!

Where can you order a dairy herd?
From a cattle-logue!

Did you hear about the pregnant lady trampolinist?
She had a bouncing baby!

On which day was the first Moon landing?
Moon-day!

What does a skeleton use to ring his friends?
Tele-bone!

What do you call a blood sucking bat that attacks pigs?
A hampire!

What do you use to catch an electric eel?
A lightning rod!

What do ponies use to send secret messages?
Horse code!

Which English king introduced wine to the country?
Alfred the Grape!

What's yellow and writes essays?
A ballpoint banana!

What do you get if you throw your computer in the sea?
Brainwaves!

Why is the letter 'K' like the end of a pig's tail?
It comes at the end of PORK!

How do you make a Venetian blind?
Cover his eyes!

How does Quasimodo carry his sandwiches?
In the Lunchpack of Notre-Dame!

What do apes use to toast bread?
A grilla!

What do posh fish put on their dining tables?
'Plaice' mats!

What do you call a crowd at a ghost football match?
Spook-tators!

Did you hear about the two fat runners?
One ran in short bursts and one ran in burst shorts!

What kind of dish holds nothing at all!
A ra-dish!

Why are giraffes inexpensive to feed?
Because their food goes a long way!

Doctor: "When did you first start to think you were a cat?"
Patient: "When I was a kitten!"

"Doctor, doctor, I feel like I'm going bald!"
"You need some fresh 'air'!"

Why is the word SMILES so long?
Because there is a mile in the middle!

Why are teachers and teddy bears similar?
They both watch you with beady little eyes!

When is a blue school book not a blue school book?
When it is read!

Which vegetable can see the best?
A potato - it has lots of eyes!

What are you going to be when you get out of school?
An old man!

What wears a white coat and melts in the Sun?
A lollipop lady!

What is the difference between electricity and lightning?
You don't pay for lightning!

What do you get when you cross the Atlantic in the Titanic?
Half way there!

What do you call a girl who lives under a cow?
Pat!

What do you call a young bee?
A bay-bee!

What do sheep heat
their homes with?
Central bleating!

How can you tell
a wolf man from
his sister?
His sister has a
shorter beard!

"Doctor, doctor, I keep
thinking I'm a guitar!"
"You are highly strung!"

What do you get when
you cross a snowman
and Dracula?
Frostbite!

What do you call the
biggest mouse in
the world?
A hippopota-mouse!

Which car do rich
people drive in China?
A Rolls Rice!

What do you call a cat
that lives in the sea?
An octopuss!

What do highwaymen
bees call out?
Your honey or your life!

When do you wrap up in brown paper and string?
On a package holiday!

What do you call a horse in striped pyjamas?
A zebra!

What is the worst cake to have in your tummy?
Stomach-cake!

Why does the sea trust no one?
Because it has often been crossed!

"Doctor, doctor, I feel like a banana!"
"Your skin is peeling!"

What does a poltergeist guard call out?
Who ghosts there?

What travels all round the world yet stays in the same corner?
A postage stamp!

What does a lady monster keep in her handbag?
Hands!

How do vampires
like their fish served?
In bat-ter!

What's the
difference between a
teacher and a train?
The train goes
"Chew chew" and the
teacher says,
"Spit that gum out!"

Who can shave all
day and still have
a beard?
A barber!

Who has a parrot that
squawks, 'Pieces of four'?
Short John Silver!

What did it say on the
alien's school report?
"This pupil's work is
out of this world!"

Why did the
teacher yell at
Humpty Dumpty?
Because he cracked
up in class!

Did you hear about the
boy who spent hours on
his homework each night?
He kept it under
his mattress!

What do foxes put on
to keep warm?
Foxgloves!

Did you hear about the school near the chicken farm?
The pupils picked up fowl language!

What does a lady snake do when she has a cold?
Viper nose!

What do you call a dance for butterflies?
A mothball!

Why did the farmer have sore feet?
A tractor ran over his corn!

When did Adam and Eve eat the apple?
Before their first date!

Did you hear about the school trip to Venice?
They came back because it was flooded!

"Doctor, doctor, my son has grown another foot!"
"Enter him in to a three-legged race!"

What do you call bees that keep dropping things?
Fumble bees!

Why did the spider
test drive a car?
He wanted to take it out
for a spin!

Why is school like
a shower?
One wrong turn and
you're in hot water!

Where do gardeners
play snooker!
In potting sheds!

Teacher: "Your
essay about your
dog is the same as
your sister's!"
Pupil: "Yes, it's the
same dog!"

What do skeletons
watch for
entertainment?
Skele-vision!

What did the angry
miller try to do?
Grind his teeth!

What is a monster's
favourite drink?
Demonade!

What kind of ships do
students travel on?
Scholarships!

Did you hear about the man who never cleaned his glasses? He gave everyone filthy looks!

What do you get when you cross a fish with an elephant? Swimming trunks!

What is a cannibal's favourite day! Chewsday!

What do invisible people say to greet each other? "Nice not to see you!"

"Waiter, Waiter, why is there mould on my lettuce?" "You said you wanted a green salad!"

"Doctor, doctor, my hair keeps falling out; give me something to keep it in!" "Here is a box!"

What does the Abominable Snowman call its kids? Chill-dren!

What do you call a one-eyed monster on a bicycle? Cycle-ops!

157

"Doctor, doctor, I want to spend all night under the bed!"
"You are a little potty!"

Why is basketball the most respectable sport?
Everyone looks up to the players!

"Knock, knock!"
"Who's there?"
"Aladdin!"
"Aladdin who?"
"Aladdin the street"

What is brown and makes a noise like a bell?
Dunngggg!

Why did the coach put sawdust on the football pitch?
He wanted to stop his team slipping out of the league!

Where do sheep go for a haircut?
The Baaaaaaarber!

How do you stop a rhino from charging?
Take away its credit cards!

Did you hear about the secretary who cut her fingers off?
She wanted to write shorthand!

158

Did you hear about
the turkey that ate
too much?
It was stuffed!

Did you hear about
the virus that went
on holiday?
It went to Germ-any!

Mother: "Did you put out the cat?"
Son: "I didn't even know it was on fire!"

Why did the river
go on a diet?
It wanted to lose a
few ponds!

What is a ghost's
favourite fairground ride?
A roller ghoster!

Did you hear about
the mean oyster?
It was shellfish!

Where do children
learn their ABC's?
At LMN-tary school!

Why did the policeman
work up a tree?
He was in special branch!

What's green and
dangerous?
A frog with a
hand grenade!

What did one teddy
say to the other
after dinner?
"I'm stuffed!"

What's black and white
and red at the bottom?
A badger with nappy rash!

How do you make
a milk shake?
Give it a good scare.

What sleeps at the
bottom of the sea?
A kipper.

How do you speak to a fish?
Drop him a line.

Why was the trout's
piano off key?
Because he couldn't find
the piano tuna!

Why was the pelican
afraid to leave the hotel?
Because it had a big bill.

How do biologists
communicate?
By 'cell' phone.

Where do aliens go to
see a film?
To Cine-mars.